We Love to Share

A Ready, Set, Go! Reader

by Liza Charlesworth
illustrated by Louise Forshaw

ISBN 978-0-545-80267-3

18 17 16 15 14   19

Printed in the U.S.A.   40
First printing, September 2014

Designed by Maria Mercado

SCHOLASTIC INC.

We share paper.

We share crayons.

We share scissors.

We share paints.

We share shapes.

We share glue.

We share stickers.

We share feathers.

We share glitter.

We share a picture!

Comprehension Boosters

1. What different things did the children share?

2. What did the children make?

3. Why is sharing a good thing to do? What do you share?

"Mine!" said Ricky. He grabbed the
rattle. Then he threw it down.
Ricky looked at the pile on the table.
Then his face lit up. He started to play.
Things went flying around in a wild
scramble.

"Here, penny, penny! Where are you,
penny?" he yelled.

Jim and I started to giggle again.
Ricky looked at us with a big grin.

"Hey!" he said. "Look what I've got!"

"Okay Ricky!" I shouted. I ran over to get my lucky penny. It wasn't my penny, though. It was a baseball card. Ricky brought it over. He made a little bow. I took the card from him and looked at it.

"Wow!" I said. It wasn't just any old card.

It was Dan Maple, my best baseball
card. "Thanks, Ricky," I said. "That's
been lost for weeks. I didn't know where
it was. That card is hard to get."

"Yes," said Ricky. "Lucky lucky."

It *was* lucky. But where was my
penny?

"I bet I know where it is," said Jim.
He picked up the end of the rug.
He peeked under it. There was just fluff
and dust. Then he picked up the other
end.

Ricky zoomed over. Jim and I got out of his way. We had to move fast. Ricky slid under the rug. All we could see was a bump.

"Wiggle wiggle," said the bump. Ricky was having fun. "Here, penny, penny! Where are you, penny?" he yelled.

Jim and I started to giggle again.

Ricky looked at us with a big grin. "Hey!" he said. "Look what I've got!"

"Thanks, Ricky!" I shouted. I ran over to get my lucky penny. It wasn't my penny, though. It was a little key.

I had never seen it. Jim had never seen it.

But Ricky was all grins. He waved the key around in the air.

"*My* key," he said. "My key for my best red box. Come on, Jim! Come on, Jill! Let's get my box."

"Now we can see what's in it," said Jim. "That box has been shut for a year."

"Yes," said Ricky. "Lucky lucky."

It *was* lucky. But where was my penny?

Ricky ran to his room. Jim and I were right behind him. Ricky ran to the table by his bed.

He had lots of boxes there. Big ones, little ones, beautiful ones, ugly ones! He picked up the box in front. It was red and had a gold handle.

"I put the key here," said Ricky. "Then I do this. Then it goes click. And now I lift up the lid. . . ."

"Hey!" said Ricky. "Look what I've got!"
And there in the box was—a penny!

It wasn't my penny, though. It was just an old, dull penny.

Then Mom came in. We told her about looking for my lucky penny. Jim told her about the places we looked. I told her about the lost things we got back. Ricky told her he felt fine. And right then, it started to rain.

"Lucky you stayed home," said Mom.

That's the end of the story.

I never did find that lucky penny.

But you know what?

I didn't need it, after all.

-le	-s	-es
dimple	dimes	boxes
giggle	ends	buses
handle	grins	passes
jingle	nickels	
jumble	odds	
little	pillows	
Maple	places	
middle	things	
nibble	weeks	
paddle		
puzzle		
rattle		
scramble		
simple		
sniffle		
Sparkle		
table		
Uncle		
wiggle		

Phonics Reader 35 ★ Words to Remember

brought   example   front   though

Phonics Reader 35 ★ Story Words

hey   ones   pennies   towels   threw   winners